TIMELESS TALES

Fables

Retold by TANA REIFF

Illustrated by CATHERINE CHAUVIN

SEP 1998

SALINAS PUBLIC LIBRARY

J
398
REI

NEW READERS PRESS

ISBN 0-88336-270-8

Copyright © 1991
New Readers Press
Publishing Division of Laubach Literacy International
Box 131, Syracuse, New York 13210-0131

All rights reserved. No part of this book may be reproduced or transmitted in any form or by any means, electronic or mechanical, including photocopying, recording, or by any information storage and retrieval system, without permission in writing from the publisher.

Printed in the United States of America

Project editor: Elizabeth Costello
Manuscript editor: Mark Legler
Designer: Patricia Rapple
Illustrator: Catherine Chauvin
Cover designers: The WD Burdick Company
Sponsoring editor: Marianne Ralbovsky

9 8 7 6 5 4 3 2

Contents

Introduction

The tales in this book go back to early Greece. A man named Aesop (EE-sop) would gather people together and tell them little stories called *fables*. Later on, the stories were written down so others could enjoy them.

A fable is a story that teaches a lesson. The lesson of the fable is called the moral of the story. For example, the moral of "The Fox and the Goat" is *Look before you leap*. The story itself tells how the goat came to learn the lesson.

Animals play the main parts in many fables. The animal may be smart, like the crow in "The Crow and the Pitcher." The animal may be silly, like the monkey in "The Monkey and the Fish." The animal may be lazy, careful, or stubborn. Many of them act a lot like people sometimes do.

Of course, in some fables people play the main parts. They are the ones who learn the lessons in "The Boy Who Cried 'Wolf'" and in "The Goose That Laid the Golden Eggs."

The main parts in some fables are played by neither people nor animals. "The Wind and the Sun" is about a game between those two forces of nature.

Because fables point out life's truths, they have lasted all these years. Fables have been told and retold many, many times in many languages. Many people have enjoyed them and learned their lessons.

The Rabbit and the Turtle

"You are a slow, old thing," the rabbit said to the turtle. "How do you get anywhere on time?"

"I'll show you," answered the turtle. "Let's run a race. Let's just see who finishes first."

"What a funny idea!" laughed the rabbit. "Run a race with a turtle? Do you think you can beat me? Ha! You're on!"

The race began. In no time at all, the rabbit ran far ahead. "I'm so far in front, I'm going to stop and take a nap," he said. "I might as well give that turtle a chance to catch up!"

Miles back, the turtle walked along. Slow were his steps. But never did he stop. Never did he rest. He just kept going.

At last, he reached the sleeping rabbit. The turtle lumbered by. The rabbit slept like a baby.

The turtle came very close to the finish line. Just then, the rabbit woke up. He jumped to his feet and dashed off. But it was too late. As fast as he was, the rabbit could not beat the turtle to the finish line. Slow as he was, the turtle won the race.

Slow and steady wins the race.

The Goose That Laid the Golden Eggs

 Far out in the country lived a man who had a goose. Now, this was not just any goose. This goose was very special, for every day she laid one beautiful golden egg.

Each day the man would come to the goose's nest to take her golden egg. He would ride into the city and sell the egg for a high price. It didn't take the man long to get rich.

However, the man was not happy with his money. Soon, he began to wish the goose would lay more eggs. That way, he could get richer faster.

He came up with an idea.

He killed the goose and cut her open. He hoped to find a lot of golden eggs inside. But, much to his surprise, he found no eggs at all! Not one. And he never got another golden egg. The goose that laid the golden eggs was dead.

**When you want too much,
you end up with nothing.**

The Crow and the Pitcher

There had been no rain for a long time. All the birds needed water to drink. A big black crow hopped along the ground looking for water. Then she spotted a pitcher. She looked inside it. There was a little bit of water at the bottom. It was probably left from the last rain.

The crow poked her beak into the neck of the pitcher. But she couldn't reach down far enough to get any water.

Then she came up with a smart idea. All around were little stones. The crow dropped the stones into the pitcher, one by one, until the water rose to the top. Then she stuck her beak into the pitcher and took a nice, long drink.

When you have a problem, use your head.

The Wind and the Sun

 Which is stronger—the wind or the sun?

"I am stronger," said the wind.

"No, I am stronger," said the sun.

"How can we find out which of us is really stronger?" asked the wind.

"Let us do this," said the sun. "Here comes a man walking down the road. Whoever can get the coat off the man is the stronger."

"All right," said the wind. "We will find out once and for all who is stronger. Will it be I, the wind, or you, the sun?"

The wind had a plan. He began to blow cold air all over the man. But the coat did not blow off. Instead, the man pulled his coat close around him. The harder the wind blew, the closer the man held his coat.

Now it was the sun's turn. The sun sent bright, warm light down onto the road. The heat from the sun made the man feel warm. He opened his coat to cool off a bit.

The light from the sun became warmer still. The man took off his hat to cool off some more.

The sun kept shining on the man. The light from the sun became even warmer. The man felt so hot that he took off his coat.

Then the man sat down under a tree. He rested until he was ready to walk again.

The sun looked down at the man. "You see," he said to the wind, "I showed that I am stronger than you. I got that coat off the man. All it took was a little time."

A gentle touch works better than force.

The
Fox
and
the
Grapes

One day a fox was taking a walk.
Along the way, he spotted a vine
growing by the side of the road.
On the vine hung a beautiful
bunch of purple grapes.

"I want those grapes!" said
the fox.

However, the grapes were hanging way up
high on the vine. The fox reached up, but he
could not get the grapes.

So he backed up a few feet. He ran right toward the grapevine. He leaped into the air, reaching for the grapes. He got a little higher on this try. But he could not reach high enough.

He backed up a few more feet. He took yet another running leap. He came within a few inches of the grapes. Still, he could not reach them.

After many tries, the fox gave up. He sat
down under the grapevine. He was feeling
pretty angry. "I didn't want those grapes
anyway," he said. "I am sure they were sour.
A bunch of sour grapes is not worth all
this trouble."

And on he walked.

Finding fault with what
you can't have is only
pretending that you
never wanted it.

The Fox and the Goat

One hot day a fox fell into a well. There was water in the well, so the fox took a long, cool drink. However, when he tried to climb out, he could not. The well was too deep.

Along came a goat. The goat saw the fox down in the well. But he did not know the fox was stuck. "How is the water?" asked the goat.

"Very fine, very fine," answered the fox. "Jump in and have a drink!"

The goat jumped right in and began to drink. Just as fast, the fox jumped on the goat's back. He used the goat to climb out of the well. Once he was out, he ran off into the woods.

Now the goat could not get out. "Help!" he cried to the fox.

The fox kept on running. "You are not a very smart goat!" he laughed. "You jumped right into the well. You didn't stop to think about how you would get back out!"

Look before you leap.

The Fox and the Stork

As you know, a stork is a bird with a long, pointed beak. Well, the fox liked to make fun of the stork's beak. He decided to play a trick on the stork.

"Won't you come to dinner?" the fox asked.

"Why, yes," said the stork.

So the stork came to dinner. When she got there, she was very hungry.

The fox had made soup for dinner. He put the soup in a big, flat dish.

The stork dipped her beak into the dish. But she could not eat the soup. The dish was just too flat. The fox ate up all the soup, and the stork went home hungry.

A few days later the stork asked the fox to dinner. When the fox got there, he was very hungry.

The stork had made fish for dinner. It smelled wonderful. The stork put the fish into a tall jar.

The fox looked at the jar. He smelled the fish. He licked the jar. But there was no way he could get his mouth down to the fish.

"What a shame! You can't eat your fish!" laughed the stork. "I guess I'll have to eat your fish myself." She stuck her long beak into the jar and ate all the fish. This time, it was the fox who went home hungry.

Don't dish out what you can't take.

The Ants and the Grasshopper

It was a beautiful fall day. A family of ants was busy, busy, busy putting away food for the long winter ahead.

Along came a hungry grasshopper. He was playing a fiddle and singing a song. "I'm one hungry little grasshopper," he said. "May I have some of your food?"

"Don't you have any food of your own?"
asked the ants. "What were you doing all
summer? We were busy finding food to
put away for the winter."

"I was too busy making music," said the
grasshopper. "I had no time to look for food!
Please, won't you give me some of yours?"

"Forget it!" said the ants. "Music is fine. We
all love music. But you can't play music all
the time. Now you come to us for food. That
isn't fair. We worked hard to find this food.
You should have worked, too!"

**There is a time for work
and a time for play.**

The Monkey and the Fish

A long, long time ago, there were no airplanes. The only way to travel over water was by boat. And many people back then took along their pets.

One time a boat crashed into a big rock. The people on board jumped into the water. Luckily for them, some big fish came along and saved the people by carrying them on their backs. The pets were not so lucky. It was more important to save the people.

On that ship was a pet monkey. The monkey wanted to be saved. So he hopped onto a fish's back before the fish could see him. The fish thought he was carrying a person. He didn't know he had a monkey on his back.

The fish tried to be friendly. "Are you from the big city?" the fish asked the monkey.

"Oh, yes," the monkey lied. "Not only do I live in the big city, but my father is the mayor."

The fish was impressed. "Is that so?" he asked. "Then you must know the King, too."

"Oh, yes," the monkey lied again. "I have dinner with the King very often. In fact, the King is my best friend."

"Wow!" said the big fish. He wanted a look at this important person riding on his back. He turned around. Only then did he see that it was a monkey, not a person! A monkey telling big lies about knowing the King!

The fish dumped the monkey into the water. Then he went off to look for someone else to save.

One lie leads to another.

The Three Bulls and the Lion

Three bulls were eating some tall green grass together. They did not know that a lion had his eye on them. A bull would make a good meal, the lion was thinking. But even a lion was no match for three strong bulls. One at a time, perhaps, but not three. So the lion lay back in the field and watched.

Just then, the bulls began fighting over one spot of grass. They got so angry that each one took off to a different corner of the field. That way, they each had their own spot of grass.

The lion saw his chance. He leaped into the field toward the first bull. Then he went for the second and the third. One by one, the lion killed all three bulls. Oh, what a fine meal the lion had that day! When he was finished, he sat down under a tree and licked his chops.

Together you are strong; apart you are not.

The
Boy
Who
Cried
"Wolf"

Once there was a boy who had a job watching sheep in the field. If ever a wolf came near the sheep, he was supposed to cry, "Wolf! Wolf!" Then people from town would come to scare the wolf away from the sheep.

Days passed, and no wolf came. The sheep did nothing but eat and sleep. The boy had nothing to do but watch them.

The boy grew tired of his job. He wanted to stir things up a bit. So he ran toward the town. "Wolf! Wolf!" he cried. The people stopped what they were doing and ran to help. When they reached the field, they found no wolf. The boy laughed and laughed. The people did not think this was funny. Back they went to their own work.

The next day, the boy tried his trick again. "Wolf! Wolf!" he cried. Again, the people from town came running. Again, they found no wolf. Again, the boy laughed and laughed.

The next day began like all the rest—no wolf, no trouble. Suddenly, a wolf really did come into the field. It ran for the sheep, killing one, two, three of them.

The boy shook all over. "Wolf! Wolf!" he cried. This time, no people came to help. They all believed the boy was up to his tricks again.

The wolf killed all the sheep. And the boy? He was never seen again.

If you tell lies, no one will believe you when you tell the truth.

The Wolf and the Lion

 One day a wolf killed a little lamb. It was a sad, ugly sight. The poor lamb did not have a chance against the big, mean wolf.

The wolf took off for home. He carried the lamb down the road. Along came a lion, who walked right up and took the lamb away from the wolf.

"Hey!" cried the wolf. "You can't take that lamb! It's mine!"

But the lion kept on walking. He did not plan to start a fight. From far enough away he turned around to look at the wolf. "Did you buy this lamb?" asked the lion.

"Why, no," answered the wolf.

"Did someone give you this lamb?" asked the lion.

"Well, no," answered the wolf.

"Well, then, how can you say it is your lamb?" asked the lion.

Here was a question to which the wolf had no answer.

What you get in a bad way will be lost in a bad way.

The Lion and the Mouse

 A grand-looking lion was taking a nap in the woods. As he slept, a little mouse walked onto his head. The lion did not wake up.

Then the mouse got stuck in the lion's fur. She tried to get free. But the lion felt the mouse and woke up. Angry as could be, he pressed his big paw right onto the mouse.

"Oh, please!" cried the mouse. "Let me go! Please let me go and someday I will find a way to help you."

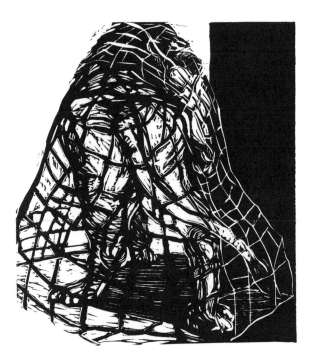

"Ha!" laughed the lion. "A little mouse help a grand lion? That is very funny."

And so, feeling sorry for the mouse, the lion let her go.

"That was very kind of you," said the mouse. "Thank you, my friend. You wait! Someday I will help you."

The lion fell back to sleep.

Days later, the lion ran into trouble. He was walking through the woods. He walked right into a hunter's net and got stuck. He poked his paws at the net. He made loud noises. But he could not get loose.

In a little while, along came that same little mouse. "Here I am to help you!" said the mouse.

"I wish you could," cried the lion. "But how? You are only a little mouse."

The mouse began to chew at the net. She chewed and chewed. She chewed until part of the net broke open. She chewed another part open, too. One more break and the lion was free!

"I didn't think a little mouse could ever help me!" said the lion. "But you did! Just as you said you would! Thank you, my friend."

A kind act is always remembered.

Belling the Cat

 You might think that a mouse family would have nothing to worry about. After all, what's so hard about being a mouse? But one family of mice had a real problem.

The problem was a cat. He was a big, mean cat. And he was always trying to catch the poor mice. He would run after them and sometimes grab one by the tail. How could these little mice ever feel safe?

Enough was enough. Something had to be done about that cat. So the mouse family all got together to talk about their problem.

"Maybe we could run away a little faster," said a young boy mouse.

"We are already running as fast as our little legs will take us," said the mother mouse.

"Maybe we could all run after the cat," said the father mouse.

"What for?" asked the grandmother mouse, who was very smart. "The cat would only run away. He would come back for us another time."

"I have an idea!" piped up the young girl mouse, who was always full of ideas. "Let's hang a bell around the cat's neck. When the cat comes near us, we will hear the bell. Then we can get away before he hurts anyone."

Everyone loved this idea. At last, the mice would be free of the cat!

Then the very smart grandmother mouse asked an important question. "Who, may I ask, will put that bell on the cat?"

**Talking is one thing;
doing is something else.**

The Country Mouse and the City Mouse

 There once was a mouse who lived in the country. Her home was under a stone wall. She lived on corn, berries, and nuts. She never went hungry.

One summer, this country mouse's cousin from the city came to visit. The country mouse laid out her best corn, berries, and nuts. But the city mouse would not eat.

"I worked so hard to get this food," said the country mouse. "Why won't you eat it?"

"Because it is country food," said the city mouse. "I would rather eat city food. Besides, it is so easy for me in the city. I never have to hunt for food. It is all left for me on the table."

"Then take me to the city with you," said the country mouse. "If I like your life, maybe I will move there."

So the two mice went to the city mouse's house. On the table, they found the leftovers of a beautiful meal. There were all kinds of fancy foods on pretty silver plates. The mice jumped up onto the table and began to eat some cheese.

Just then, they heard a cat. They jumped off the table and ran into a hole in the wall.

When the cat left, the two mice jumped back onto the table. They began to eat some meat.

Just then, a dog ran into the room and barked at them. Again, the mice jumped off the table and ran back into the hole.

When the dog left, the mice came out of the hole. The city mouse started toward the table. The country mouse started toward the door.

"Where are you going?" the city mouse asked her cousin.

"Home to the country," said the country mouse. "You have pretty plates and fancy food. But I would rather eat in peace."

It is better to be poor and at peace than rich and afraid.

The Wolf and the House Dog

 Once there was a wolf who lived in a city. She lived on whatever food she could find. Every night she would come by the houses looking for food. But she didn't find much food there. Why not? Because many people in this city had dogs. If there was extra food, the house dogs got it. The hungry wolf was nothing but skin and bones.

The wolf made friends with a house dog. "You could be eating better," said the dog.

"How?" asked the wolf.

"Come and live like me," said the house dog. "You can eat the food the people throw away. You can beg from their table. Be nice to them and they will give you plenty of food."

All of this sounded very good to the wolf. But then she looked more closely at the dog. She saw that the fur around the dog's neck was missing.

"What is wrong with your neck?" the wolf asked.

"That is where they tie me up behind the house," said the dog.

"Tie you up?" cried the wolf. "You cannot run free any time you want?"

"Oh, no," said the dog. "Being tied up is part of my life."

"That is a high price to pay for your food," said the wolf. "I would rather work a little harder and run free."

And off she ran.

Freedom is often worth the price.

SALINAS PUBLIC LIBRARY

3 3550 00538 8272

SALINAS PUBLIC LIBRARY

JAN 1993
Received
John Steinbeck
Library